THE NOTEBOOK OF STEPHEN CRANE

THE NOTEBOOK OF STEPHEN CRANE

Edited by Donald J. Greiner and Ellen B. Greiner

A JOHN COOK WYLLIE MEMORIAL PUBLICATION

Library of Congress Catalog
Card Number 68–55613
Printed in the
United States of America

INTRODUCTION

Edwin Mitchell announced in 1935 the existence of a Stephen Crane Notebook[1] which Crane probably kept during his 1892–1894 sojurn in New York, but its contents remained a mystery until 1956. In that year R. W. Stallman printed in the *Bulletin* of the New York Public Library two complete sketches and part of a third from the previously unknown material in the Notebook,[2] then a part of the Clifton Waller Barrett Collection now housed in the University of Virginia Library. One of the sketches published in the *Bulletin,* "Heard on the Street Election Night," and most of the others in the Notebook formed early drafts for material which Crane published between 1894 and 1900. In 1966 Stallman and E. R. Hagemann gathered together these published pieces and printed them in a collection of Crane's New York City sketches.[3] Although the vast majority of the material in their collection was previously published by Crane, two sketches from the Notebook, "The Art Student's League Building" and "Matinee Girls," were not. The Notebook remains the only known source for these additions to the Crane canon.

[1] Edwin Mitchell, *Art of Authorship* (1935). Reference from R. W. Stallman, *Stephen Crane: An Omnibus* (New York, 1957), p. xxxii.

[2] "Matinee Girls," "Election Night: New York," "The Art Student's League," and a short literary note. See Stallman, "Stephen Crane: Some New Stories," *Bulletin* of the New York Public Library, LX (September, 1956), 455–462.

[3] *The New York City Sketches of Stephen Crane and Related Pieces,* ed. R. W. Stallman and E. R. Hagemann (New York, 1966).

Despite the value of both the 1956 article and the 1966 collection, neither offers a correct reading of "The Art Student's League Building" or "Matinee Girls" because these sketches are transcribed from photocopies rather than from a direct examination of the originals in the Notebook. The condition of the Notebook demands transcription from the manuscript itself because the cheap paper pages are deteriorating and because Crane wrote in pencil. Stallman's use of photocopies for the 1956 reproduction of "Matinee Girls" results in missed punctuation, spelling, and word sequence. In the 1966 collection, Stallman and Hagemann failed to correct these errors, evidently because they transferred the 1956 photocopy reproduction of "Matinee Girls" to their collection without examining the Notebook.[4]

The reproductions of "The Art Student's League Building" create even greater confusion. Published only partially in 1956, that transcription also misses punctuation and spelling. Although several of these minor punctuation errors were corrected when the complete sketch was published in 1966, new errors were made that were

[4] In the second sentence of "Matinee Girls," for example, the 1956 and the 1966 versions read, "To read of them, you would think they provided every theatre in New York but really I don't think them a very familiar type." But Crane wrote, "To read of them, you would think they crowded every theatre in New York but really I don't think them a very familiar type."

not in the 1956 article.[5] While Stallman and Hagemann may have given a closer look to the 1956 photocopy of "The Art Student's League Building" in an attempt to give a correct transcription, they again transferred the faulty photocopy text to their collection without examining the Notebook. These errors leave "Matinee Girls" and "The Art Student's League Building" fresh material for the Crane student. The remaining pieces in the Notebook, which is published here as a whole for the first time, are especially valuable because they provide an opportunity for comparison between Crane's early drafts and the finished products.

Comparisons of this sort offer insights into Crane's method of working up notes for final publication. An examination of the Notebook supports the claims of Crane's biographers that he was more of a conscious artist than he sometimes liked to admit. During his years in and about Park Row in New York, he took notes on specific dramatic situations, most of which he later revised and expanded into formal sketches. Despite these writing habits, Crane often took pains to suggest that he was

[5] For example, the 1956 article correctly reproduces Crane's spelling of "puritanical," while the 1966 collection spells it "puritannical."

an inspired writer, one whose words flowed from his pen without prior thought or planning.[6] John Berryman records the story of a Crane visit in February, 1894, to Hamlin Garland. Crane arrived with a roll of "lines" or poems for Garland's inspection. Completely amazed, Garland asked if Crane had any more. " 'I have four or five up here,' the poet pointed to his temple, 'all in a little row.' " When Garland asked him to write one, Crane sat down and wrote the poem beginning "God fashioned the ship of the world carefully." According to Garland, the poem "flowed from his pen," though Crane insisted that he had never before written it down or consciously thought about the word arrangement.[7] Whether this particular poem was a product of unpremeditated inspiration is open to question, but a look at a complete poem in the Notebook clearly exemplifies Crane's habit of revision. Although there are only four word changes between the draft in the Notebook and the final published form, the deleted and added words prove that Crane consciously worked on the poem.

Similarly there can be little doubt that Crane

[6] See Stallman, *Crane: An Omnibus*, pp. xxxi–xxxii for Crane's thoughts on inspired writing. See also Joseph Conrad's Introduction to Thomas Beer, *Stephen Crane: A Study in American Letters* (New York, 1924), esp. p. 27. Conrad comments on Crane's apparent ease in writing.

[7] John Berryman, *Stephen Crane* (New York, 1950), pp. 75–76.

planned and arranged most of his better prose pieces. Referring to *The Red Badge of Courage*, Berryman draws on an account written by R. G. Vosburgh, a friend with whom Crane stayed while working on parts of that novel. Vosburgh notes that "every incident and phase of character" in *The Red Badge* was discussed before Crane worked it into the manuscript.[8] The novel, of course, demanded more planning than the short poems, but Vosburgh's comments help to underline the discrepancy between Crane's true writing habits and the image he liked to put forth.

The Notebook contradicts Crane's assertions that revisions are signs of dishonesty in the writer. Not only does it prove that Crane took notes before working his sketches into final form, but even more significant, the Notebook reveals revisions within the notes themselves, further evidence of Crane's conscientious writing. In the Notebook draft of "The Park Row Restaurant," for example, Crane cancelled only eighteen words, but those cancellations took him eighteen steps away from the role of purely inspired artist. Crane finished the first page of

[8] Berryman, pp. 72–73.

"A Street Scene" before he rejected his initial draft and started over again on the next leaf. Isolated fragments in the Notebook, such as the unnamed scene on leaf 37^{r}–leaf 39^{r}, suggest that Crane recorded dramatic situations as they occurred to him with the intention of later incorporating them into complete stories. The revisions in the draft of "The Duel That Was Not Fought" show that Crane altered the dialogue to bring it closer to colloquial speech. At first giving such words as "you" and "that" their conventional spelling, he later changed them to "yeh" and "dat," thereby unifying a character's speech with his personality.

A comparison of the opening lines of "A Desertion" in both manuscript and final form illustrates Crane's careful revisions. In the Notebook version Crane fails to realize his setting. Instead of helping the reader visualize the dimly lighted, dirty, and grotesque tenement hall, he begins the sketch with a brief conventional description of the hallway. More important, this early draft lacks the realistic dialogue of the published form which enables Crane to set up a contrast between the gossiping women's view of the young girl and the reader's. The Notebook version suggests merely that the women are gossiping, while the final version exchanges suggestion for actual dialogue:

> In the dark hall-way of the tenement three women were quarreling animatedly. Their gestures made enormous shadows that, further back, mingled in terrific combat.
>
> A young girl came from the street and brushed past them on her way upstairs. [Notebook]
>
> The yellow gas-light that came with an effect of difficulty through the dust-stained windows on either side of the door gave strange hues to the faces and forms of the three women who stood gabbling in the hallway of the tenement. They made rapid gestures, and in the background their enormous shadows mingled in terrific conflict.
>
> "Ay, she ain't so good as he thinks she is, I'll bet. He can watch over 'er an' take care of 'er all he pleases, but when she wants t' fool 'im, she'll fool 'im. An' how does he know she ain't foolin' 'im now? [9]

In addition to making available early drafts of pieces published later, the Notebook helps to clarify the

[9] *The Work of Stephen Crane*, ed. Wilson Follett (New York, 1925), XI, 97.

problem of Crane's literary creed. Literary critics and historians have insisted for years that Crane belongs with the naturalists,[10] even though he sided with the realists, then the impressionists. While formulating his own literary principles, Crane apparently thought of his work as realism in the vein of Howells and Garland, for he saw in their writing a definite reaction against what he called the "clever" school. But as many readers have noted, the dominating characteristic of Crane's style is irony, and the sophisticated use of irony is not to be found in Howells and Garland. Garland, moreover, insisted that a realist was also an optimist, a maxim with which Crane had little sympathy.

Probably Crane allied himself with Howells and Garland because he believed realism to be a good approach to artistic truth, and because he saw realism gain respectability with Howells' leadership. But what Crane really seemed to be striving for was literary impressionism. He often defined what impressionism meant to him, and Berryman quotes Crane's words, recorded by a friend, which point to the reasons for his faith in it:

[10] For example, *The Literary History of the United States*, ed. Spiller, Thorp et al. (New York, 1946), asserts that Crane was a pioneer of American naturalism (p. 1026).

"Impressionism was his faith. Impressionism, he said, was truth, and no man could be great who was not an impressionist, for greatness consisted in knowing the truth. He said that he did not expect to be great himself, but he hoped to get near the truth."[11] Since impressionistic writing lacked the status of realism, Crane sided with Howells and Garland, who, it seemed to him, were also trying to get at life's truth.

The Notebook verifies his affirmation of impressionism. Although he earned his living as a journalist during the years in New York, the Notebook lacks the on-the-spot reporting and minute description characteristic of pure realism and naturalistic doctrine. The only evidence of direct reporting is his notes on election night in New York which he later published as "Heard on the Street Election Night." But even here his emphasis falls not so much on reporting the facts as on capturing the speech habits of the crowd. Colloquial speech obviously fascinated Crane, and the Notebook shows that he deliberately cultivated his talent for rendering it in writing.

Also unlike the naturalists, Crane does not use de-

[11] See Berryman, pp. 52–55. See also James B. Colvert, "The Origins of Stephen Crane's Literary Creed," *Texas Studies in English*, XXXIV (1955), 179–188. Colvert argues convincingly that Crane's first serious thinking about the art of fiction stems from his reading of Kipling's *The Light That Failed.*

tail and description to stress man's lack of free will in an existence which overwhelms him. His descriptions set scenes and support tone, but they are not used to express a deterministic philosophy. Between the Notebook version of "The Duel That Was Not Fought" and the published story, for example, Crane revised his plan so that a description of a Bowery adventure turns into a mock-heroic tale.

Crane's descriptions in the Notebook stress not what an object or action really is, but the impression of the way it "seems to be." The Art Student's League Building "is plastered with signs, and wears sedately the air of being what it is not." And in "A Street Scene," men "in the foremost rank bended down eagerly anxious to see everything. Others behind them crowded savagely like starving men fighting for bread." To give the reader certain impressions of a scene, Crane relies on colors and images which become set pieces in his writing. The "dark hall-way of the tenement" and "crimson light" of the kitchen stove in "A Desertion" also turn up in *Maggie* and *George's Mother*. Images of corpses and shocked observers set the tone in "A Desertion" and "A Street Scene," as well as in *The Red Badge* and "An Upturned Face." The phrase "assassin-like" in "A Street Scene" is a consistently used set piece in Crane, and variations on it form key passages in his poems.

The opening lines of "A Street Scene" illustrate the impressionistic setting Crane gave his New York pieces. Tired workers crowd the streets, forming a mass of nameless faces. They seem to be a procession as they all move in one general direction, from shop to home. Lights from the stores and street lamps illuminate the whole affair, and a hot dinner becomes the reward for a hard day's work: "It was nearly six o'clock in the evening and this street, which led to one of the East River Ferries was crowded with laborers, men and shop women, hurrying to their dinners, made more eager by the recollections of their toil and by the shop-windows, glaring with light, suggesting those. . . ." This basic scene fron the Notebook can be found in *George's Mother*, "The Men in the Storm," "An Experiment in Misery," "Travels in New York," and others, and in each case it is the overall impression, not the literal fact, that that Crane hopes to create with his description.

The text which follows is a diplomatic reprint, an exact reproduction of the original Notebook except for differences in type, spacing, lining, and pagination. The manuscript has been transcribed in the final form that Crane gave it, but notes are included for each leaf to indicate the changes he made.

Since we do not provide notes to indicate the differences between the drafts of these sketches and their printed texts, the locations of the first published texts are given here to aid the reader who wishes to check variants. All seven of the major sketches have been reprinted in Stallman and Hagemann whose book also lists the places of first publication. Titles and publication dates are: "The Art Student's League Building" (unpublished by Crane), "The Duel That Was Not Fought" (New York *Press*, December 9, 1894), "Matinee Girls" (unpublished by Crane), "The Park Row Restaurant" (New York *Press*, October 28, 1894), "Heard on the Street Election Night" (New York *Press*, November ?,

1894), "A Desertion" (*Harper's*, November, 1900), and "A Street Scene" (New York *Press*, December 2, 1894). The Notebook version of Crane's poem "Little birds of the night" has also been published, but Wilson Follett, editor of *The Collected Poems of Stephen Crane* (New York, 1930), was unaware of its existence. Vincent Starrett and Ames W. Williams, in their *Stephen Crane: A Bibliography* (Glendale, 1948), note that the poem was first published in 1932 by the Harvard Press. Daniel G. Hoffmann later published it in the Appendix to his *The Poetry of Stephen Crane* (New York, 1957).

The Notebook itself is made of cheap paper measuring 22 x 13 cm. with 17–18 red lines per page. There are 76 unnumbered leaves, of which 17 are torn out. It is bound at the top with flimsy cardboard covers, and on the inside back cover the name "Stephen Crane" is printed upside down in light pencil. Next to "Crane" is a sticker with the name of "Harry Bacon Collamore," who owned the Notebook before Barrett. Underneath these names four, possibly five, lines of writing have been heavily erased.

Two problems make it difficult to determine the side of the Notebook on which Crane began writing. First the binding is plain on both sides, neither side having a manufacturer's title which usually points to the first page. Second, Crane began a new sketch on the first page following both halves of the binding; he could have started at either end, leaf 1^r or leaf 59^v. The leaves ripped out of the Notebook between leaf 48^r and leaf 49^r provide the chief clue to the order of composition and to the correct pagination. In the sketch beginning on leaf 46^r (later developed into "The Duel That Was Not Fought"), these missing leaves interrupt the continuity. The story jumps from "He sat," the final words on leaf 48^r, to "him with swords," the first words on leaf 49^r, with ten leaves missing between the two. It seems likely, then, that Crane began writing on this side of the Notebook, and that he tore out the leaves while writing on the verso side, thus disturbing the sketch's continuity.

With the exception of one leaf (leaf 59), Crane wrote consecutively on the rectos. He then reversed the Notebook and began writing again on the versos. The number of each Notebook leaf is indicated in brackets. The first page is designated [leaf 1^{r}], then [leaf 2^{r}], and so on through the rectos. As the Notebook is reversed, the leaf numbering begins [leaf 59^{v}], [leaf 59^{r}], [leaf 58^{v}], [leaf 57^{v}], and so on back to the first leaf.

The contents for the 59 leaves are in the following order: "Literary Notes" leaf 1^{r}–leaf 3^{r}; "The Art Student's League Building" leaf 4^{r}–leaf 14^{r}; blank leaves 15–17, leaf 18^{r}; poem leaf 19^{r}–leaf 20^{r}; blank leaf 21^{r}–leaf 27^{r}; address and number leaf 28^{r}–leaf 29^{r}; blank leaf 30^{r}–leaf 36^{r}; story fragment leaf 37^{r}–leaf 39^{r}; blank leaf 40^{r}–leaf 45^{r}; draft of "The Duel That Was Not Fought" leaf 46^{r}–leaf 53^{r}; blank leaf 54^{r}–leaf 58^{r}.

The Notebook was reversed and writing begins again on leaf 59^{v}: "Matinee Girls" leaf 59^{v}–leaf 59^{r}–leaf 58^{v}; draft of "The Park Row Restaurant" leaf 58^{v}–leaf 49^{v}; poem fragment leaf 49^{v}; blank leaf 48^{v}; draft of "Heard on the Street Election Night" leaf 47^{v}–leaf 42^{v}; draft of "A Desertion" leaf 41^{v}–leaf 38^{v}; draft of "A Street Scene" leaf 37^{v}–leaf 18^{v}; blank leaves 17–15 and leaf 14^{v}–leaf 1^{v}.

Seventeen leaves are missing: six leaves between 16 and 17; one leaf between 17 and 18; ten leaves between 48 and 49.

Spelling, grammar, punctuation, and capitalization are Crane's with two slight exceptions: we have silently crossed his occasionally uncrossed t's, and removed circles from around periods. Crane also drew several lines throughout the Notebook to designate either the end of a sketch or the separation of speakers. Termination signs [#] are on leaves 14^{r}, 58^{v}, and 49^{v}. The short pencil lines are on leaves 47^{v}–42^{v}, and 18^{v}. We have silently removed these marks.

There is a pencil scratch on a short flap turned over the top of leaf 59^{v}. Except for a few marks, Crane wrote entirely in pencil. Pencil changes have been noted when obvious, as well as the writing of others besides Crane.

Attempts to date the Notebook exactly are still somewhat uncertain. Publication dates of four sketches–"The Park Row Restaurant," "Heard on the Street Election Night," "A Street Scene," and "The Duel That Was Not Fought"–indicate that Crane kept the Notebook in the latter part of 1894. Berryman notes, however, that the New York *Press*, which published these sketches, did not print until the following October three others which Crane had written by April, 1894.[12] All that is known is that Crane was in and about the Park Row section of New York during 1892–94.

We wish to thank Mr. Clifton Waller Barrett for his generous permission to reproduce the Notebook from his magnificent collection of American Literature. We are also grateful to Professor Richard Peck of Temple University and Professor James Colvert of the University of Georgia. Both have read the manuscript and have offered valuable critical suggestions. For bibliographical assistance in the preparation of the manuscript we thank Professors Fredson Bowers and Lester Beaurline.

Donald J. Greiner
Ellen B. Greiner

University of South Carolina
Columbia

[12] See Berryman, p. 83.

THE NOTEBOOK OF STEPHEN CRANE

[leaf 1r]

Literary Notes.

Editor Jones has neatly papered his hall bed-room with Brilliant T. Hodgson's story entitled: "Love's Dream."

Jones] *the following words* 'of the' *are deleted*

[leaf 2^{r}]

In Brief.

As Peter Petersen, 32, of 963 East 67th St was viewing a base ball game he was mistaken for the umpire and killed.

The new apartment-house on West 57th Street is so great in height that the cellar is seven stories from the ground.

It is rumored that the people of Brooklyn have petitioned the legislature for forty-two new bridges across the East River. Meanwhile, escape will be facilitated by pneumatic tubes.

963] '9' *written over* '3'
East] *written over* 'West'
house] *interlined*
West] 'We' *written over* 'Ea'
Street] 'S' *written over* 's'
be] *interlined*

[leaf 3r]

The Bartholdi Statue has written to a friend that the twin lights at Navesink are two fine bouncing youngsters, bright as buttons.

the] *interlined*
lights] *the* 's' *is added; Crane originally wrote* 'light'

[leaf 4[r]]

Since the Art Student's League moved to the fine new building on West 57th St., there remains nothing but the consolation of historical value for the old structure that extends from No 143 to No 147 East 23[d] St. This building with it's common-place front is as a matter of fact one of the landmarks of American art. The old place once rang with the voices of a crowd

line 1] *this leaf originally began two lines above with the words* 'There was a ball in' *which Crane deleted; on the following line there is the beginning of an illegible word which is also deleted*

to] *the following words* 'their fine' *are deleted*

common-place] *a following* 'commercial' *is deleted*

voices of] *a following* 'one' *is deleted*

[leaf 5r]

of art students who in those days past built their ideals of art-schools upon the most approved Parisian models and it is fact generally unknown to the public that this staid puritanical old building once contained about all that was real in the Bohemian quality of New York. The exterior belies the interior in a tremendous degree. It is plastered with signs, and wears sedately the air of being what it is not.

to the] *a following* 'building' *is deleted*
York.] *the following words* 'In th[e]' *are deleted*

[leaf 6r]

The interior however is a place of slumberous corridors rambling in puzzling turns and curves. The large studios rear their brown rafters over scenes of lonely quiet. Gradually the tinkers, the tailors, and the plumbers who have captured the ground floor are creeping toward those dim ateliers above them. One by one the

slumberous] *the following letters* 'ram' *are deleted*
curves.] *the following letters* 'throu' *are deleted*
studios] *the following words* 'once the abode are now occupied by quiet' *are deleted; the words were probably two separate entries, with* 'once the abode' *deleted first, then* 'are now occupied by quiet'
rafters] *a following* 'toward' *is deleted*
have] *the following letters* 'crep' *are deleted*
creeping] *a following* 'up' *is deleted*

[leaf 7r]

besieged artists give up the struggle and the time is not far distant when the conquest of the tinkers, the tailors and the plumbers will be complete.

Nevertheless, as long as it stands, the old building be to a great many artists of this country a place endeared to them by the memory of many an escapade of the old student days when the boys of the life class

line 1] *this leaf originally began* 'artists give' *which was written on the line above* 'besieged artists' and then *deleted*
struggle] *a following period is deleted*
and the] *the following letters* 'con' *are deleted*
plumbers] 'lu' *written over what is probably* 'in'
student] *Crane originally wrote* 'students' *and then deleted the* 's'

[leaf 8r]

used to row gaily with the boys of the "preparatory antique" in the narrow halls. Every one was gay, joyous, and youthful in those blithe days and the very atmosphere of the old place cut the austere and decorous elements out of a man's heart and made him rejoice when he could devide his lunch of sandwhiches with the model

Who does not remember the incomparable "soap slides," of those days when

austere] *a following 'q' is deleted*

[leaf 9ʳ]

the whole class in the hour of rest, slid whooping across the floor one after another. The water and soap with which the brushes were washed used to make fine ice when splashed upon the floor and the hopes of America in art have taken many a wild career upon the slippery stretch. And who does not remember the little man who attempted the voyage when seated in a tin-wash-basin and who came to grief and arose covered with soap

another.] *the following words* 'upon the' *are deleted*
hopes] *interlined above deleted* 'class future'

[leaf 10r]

and deluged the studio with profanity.

Once when the woman's life class bought a new skeleton for the study of anatomy, they held a very swagger function in their class room and christened it "Mr Jolton Bones" with great pomp and ceremony. Up in the boy's life class the news of the ceremony created great excitement. They were obliged to hold a rival function without delay. And the series

bought a] *the followng letters* 'bran' *are deleted*
function] *the* 'i' *is added*
room and] *a following* 'created' *is deleted*

[leaf 11r]

of great pageants, ceremonials, celebrations and fetes which followed replete with vivid color and gorgeous action. The Parisian custom, exhaustively recounted in "Trilby" of requiring each new member of a class to make a spread for his companions was faithfully followed. Usually it consisted of beer, crackers and brie cheese.

After the Art Student's League moved to Fifty-

followed] *the following words* 'those are' *are deleted*
gorgeous] *the following letters* 'pl' *are deleted*
action.] *the following letters* 'Ther' *are deleted*
custom,] *a following* 'in' *is deleted*
member] *the following words* 'to make' *are deleted*
After] 'A' *written over* 'W'

[leaf 12r]

Seventh St., the life classes of the National Academy of Design school moved in for a time and occasionally the old building was alive with it's old uproar and it's old spirit After their departure, the corridors settled down to dust and quiet. Infrequently of a night one could pass a studio door and hear the cheerful rattle of half of a dozen tongues, hear a guitar twinkling

school] *the* 'c' *is added*
spirit] *a following period and* 'but' *are deleted*
After] *a following* 'that' *is deleted*
down] *the following words* 'again to their' *are deleted*
hear] *a following* 'one' *and the letter* 'v' *are deleted*

[leaf 13ʳ]

an accompaniment to a song, see a mass of pipe smoke cloud the air. But this too vanished and now one can only hear the commercial voices of the tinkers, the tailors and the plumbers.

In the top-most and remotest studio there is an old beam which bears this line from Emerson in half-obliterated chalk marks: "Congratulate yourselves if you have done something strange

accompaniment] *the second* 'm' *written over* 'e'

plumbers.] *following the period is the beginning of what seems to be an* 'I'

[leaf 14r]

and extravagant and broken the monotony of a decorous age." It is a memory of the old days.

[leaves 15–17 are blank; leaf 18r is blank. Between 16 and 17 six leaves are torn out; between 17 and 18 one leaf is torn out.]

[leaf 19r]

Little birds of the night
Aye, they have much to tell
Perching there in rows
Blinking at me with their serious eyes
Recounting of flowers they have seen and loved
    Of meadows and groves: of the distance
And pale sands at the foot of the sea
And breezes that fly in the leaves

line 1] *poem written in heavy dark pencil*
Aye,] 'Flew' *is deleted on the line above* 'Aye'
groves] *interlined above deleted* 'lands'
sands at] 'at' *written over* 'by'; 'by' *is deleted and possibly* 'at'

[leaf 20^r]

They are vast in experience
These little birds that come in the night

They] 'And' *deleted on the line above* 'They'

[leaves 21^{r}–27^{r} are blank.]

[leaf 28^r]

G. W. Lawrence 312 West 22^d St.

line 1] *written upside down in very light pencil with pencil line above and below*

[leaf 29r]

42

line 1] '42' *written upside down and underlined*

[leaves 30ᵛ–36ʳ are blank.]

[leaf 37ʳ]

In the midnight silence of the bed-chamber, a man's voice rang angrily while from the other pillow over next to the wall, there came a sound of low sobbing.

"You haven't got any sense at all," said the man. "If you were ever born with any, you've lost it in the shuffle somehow. What did you want to lie to me for, hey?" He sat up suddenly and sent this question forward fiercely. Then his voice dropped again to a monotone

lie to] 'to' *interlined above deleted* 'for'
for] *interlined*
and] *a following* 'swung' *is deleted*

[leaf 38r]

of intense bitterness, menace, despair, rage. "You lied, didn't you? Lied—lied like a common woman of the streets. Didn't you, now? Didn't you?" He paused a moment. Finally a woful girl's voice said: "Yes."

"Yes, lied to me! Didnt you know I'd catch you? Didnt you know I'd catch you, blast your wooden head? Yet you lied! Like a thief! How do you ever expect me to take your word again? Say? Do you expect me to trust you?

moment.] *a following* 'and' *is deleted*
head?] '?' *written over a period*
Like] 'L' *written over* 'l'
do] 'o' *written over* 'id'
expect] *a following* 'to' *is deleted*

[leaf 39r]

Do you know what your word is worth to me now? Do you know? It isnt worth that?

[leaves 40^{r}–45^{r} are blank.]

[leaf 46^{r}]

Mike Tulligan and two friends went into a corner-saloon to get drinks. There was a good deal of polished wood to be seen from the outside and everything gleamed in the mellow rays of the lights. It was a better saloon than they were used to over in their own East Side but they did not mind it. They entered and sat down at one of the little tables that were in a row parallel to the bar. They

into a] 'a' *interlined above deleted* 'the'

[leaf 47r]

ordered beer and then sat blinking stolidly at the decorations, the bar-tender and the other customers. When anything transpired they discussed it with dazzling frankness and what they said of it was as free as air to the other people in the saloon. When it became midnight there happened to be but three men besides themselves and the bar-tender in the place. Two of these were well-dressed New Yorkers who smoked cigars rapidly and swung back in their chairs

discussed it]   'it' *interlined*

[leaf 48r]

occupying themselves with themselves in the usual manner and never betraying by a wink of an eye-lid that they knew anybodyelse existed. The third man was a lithe little Cuban with miraculously small feet and hands, and with the faintest touch of down upon his youthful upper lip. As he lifted his cigarette from time to time to his lips, his little finger crooked in dainty fashion and one could see the flashes of light in an emerald. He sat

themselves with] 'w' *written over the beginning of an illegible letter*
was] *a following* 'an' *is deleted*
Cuban with] *a following* 'a' *is deleted*
crooked] *a following* 'out' *is deleted*
one] *interlined above a caret*

[leaf 49r; between leaves 48 and 49 ten leaves are torn out.]

him with swords. He'd kill you in about a minute."

But never an inch did Patsey give way. "Well, I'll give 'im a go at it, anyhow," he said, stoutly. "I'll give 'im a go at it anyhow an' I'll stay wid 'im as long as I kin."

As for the Cuban, his lithe, little body was quivering in an ecstasy of the muscles. His face was radiant was joy and his eyes shot a murderous gloating gleam upon Patsey. "Ah! Ah! He will fight me! Ah!" He bended

inch] *a following* 'to' *is deleted*
for the] *a following* 'little' *is deleted*
body was] *a following* 'fairly' *is deleted*

[leaf 50r]

unconscously in the attitude of a practised, skilful fencer. "Ah, the brrute! The brrute! I will stick him like pig."

The two well-dressed men, grinning broadly, were having a great time with Patsey. "Why, you infernal idiot, this man would slice you all up. You better jump off the bridge if you want to die. You wouldn't stand a ghost of a chance to live ten seconds."

Patsey made one persistent retort. "Well, if he wants to fight with swords, I'll give 'im a go at it, anyhow."

unconscously] *an* 'i' *following the* 'sc' *is deleted*

seconds." Patsey] *the following words are deleted:* 'was as honest and serious as dai'; *the* 'as' *is interlined above an* 'a'

lines 9, 10] *these two lines are written on one line of the Notebook* ('Retort' . . . go')

[leaf 51r]

One man said: "Well have you got a sword? Do you know what a sword is? Have you got a sword?"

"No, I aint got none," said Patsey, honestly, "but I kin git one." Then he added valiantly [']'An' d – d quick, too."

The two men laughed. "Why, can't you understand that it would be pure suicide for you to fight with swords with this fellow?"

"Dat's all right! If he wants to fight with swords, he'll git it! Dat's all!"

honestly,] *a period before the comma is deleted*

"An' d—d] *the manuscript is torn at the quotation marks before 'An" so that only one of the marks is legible*

fellow?] *the '?' is squeezed in under the quotation marks*

"Dat's] 'D' *written over* 'Th'

[leaf 52r]

The little Cuban burst out excitedly: “Ah, come on! Come on! We can take cab! Ah, you big calf, I will stick you very pretty! Ah, you will look very beautiful, very beautiful. Ah, come on, we will stop at my hotel. I have weapons there!”

“Yeh will, will yeh, yeh bloomin’ little black Dago,” cried Patsey in enraged reply to the personal part of the Cuban’s speech. He stepped forward fiercely. “Git yer d – d swords! Git em

excitedly] ‘t’ *written over* ‘d’
“Yeh] ‘eh’ *written over* ‘ou’
yer] ‘er’ *written over* ‘ou’

[leaf 53r]

I'll fight wi che! Go ahn Git 'em! I'll fight wid anyting! See? I'll fight yeh wid a knife an' fork if yeh say so, I'll fight yeh standin' up er sittin' down! I'll fight yeh in h – l, see?" This intense oration Patsey delivered with sweeping gestures, his hands stretched out eloquently, his body leaning forward, his jaw thrust out.

The wrath in the little Cuban's

anyting!] *an 'h' after 't' is deleted*
fight yeh] 'yeh' *interlined*
delivered] *interlined*
out] *a following 'in' is deleted*
eloquently,] 't' *written over an illegible letter*

[leaves 54^{r}–58^{r} are blank.]

[leaf 59^{v}]

Here are some matinee girls. To read of them, you would think they crowded every theatre in New York but really I don't think them a very familar type. I often wonder too if they are so ridiculous as we are told to believe. My curiosity over-came me so far once that I listened to the conversation of two of them.
As a matter of fact, it was much more rational than that of the man at my elbow who was talking of himself. I have wondered if they were an exception. I believe they were not and for the following formidabl[e]

once] *interlined*
my] *interlined above a caret*
himself] 'him' *written over* 'my'
formidable] *the final letter is probably an* 'e', *but because the manuscript is damaged, it is difficult to be sure*

[leaf 59r]

reason.

After you get a fact firmly into the public mind it has ceased to be true in many cases. The public began to be told long ago that it worshipped actors, men of paint and cloth, who were so human that in reality after the play they were likely to sup on welsh rabbits and beer. Just as the public came to believe it, it ceased to be. Today, a man, or a matinee girl too, sees actor and beer and welsh rabbit all together

true] *a following period is deleted*
public] *a following* 'was' *is deleted*
they] *interlined*
likely] *the following words* 'as not' *are deleted*
beer.] *a following* 'The' *is deleted*
or] *interlined above deleted* 'and'

[leaf 58^{r}]

and has not an idea that a man six feet can live on bunches of violets.

"Whenever I come into a place of this sort I am reminded of the Battle of Gettysburg," said the stranger. We were seated in one of the Park Row restaurants during the noon-hour. "I think if Pickett and his men charged in here they would be trampled under foot before they could get a biscuit. I come in here for the excitement. I feel a thrill [a]nd exhilaration during the

line 2] *blue pencil marking,* (<), *on right side of page*

line 3] 'The Park Row Resturant' *is written between lines 2 and 3 in handwriting and spelling unlike Crane's; because this title is squeezed between two lines and written over Crane's designation* (#) *for the end of the previous sketch, it is safe to say that the title was added sometime after the sketch was written and probably by someone other than Crane; in the margin,* 'Sent to P. R. [T]' *is written in the same hand and pencil as* 'The Park Row Resturant'. The initials P. R. refer to Crane's agent, Paul Reynolds.

one of the] 'the' *interlined*

and] *the first letter is probably an* 'a', *but because the manuscript is damaged, it is difficult to be sure*

[leaf 57v]

2

noon hour in here such as I might have felt if I had stood upon the summit of Little Round Top and over-looked the battle in some safe manner. It is a frightful struggle. I have often wished to induce Detaille to come to this country and get a subject for a melee that would make his frenzied Franco-Prussian battle-scenes look innocent!"

We were obliged to put our heads close together or the strangers remarks would have never have been known. Even as he spoke more men were thronging in from the streets,

in here] *the number '2' is interlined above the space between* 'in' *and* 'here'; *the numbering in this sketch is in Crane's handwriting, but in lighter pencil than that of the sketch, suggesting that the numbering was done after the sketch was complete*

might have] *interlined above a caret*

had] *interlined*

of] *the following words* 'Cemetery Ridge' are deleted

make] *interlined above deleted* (put)

Franco-Prussian] *the following words* 'scenes to scorn' *are deleted*

[leaf 56ʳ]

3
clapping their hats upon pegs and sitting down with more or less violence. The men already seated were eating with terrible speed or else casting stormy glances after the waiters.

"Hey! Did you forget those chops?"

"Waiter! Here! A napkin, please!"

"Hurry up that pie, will you, old man!"

"Got that mutton-stew yet?"

"Butter-cakes and coffee! Certainly! About ten minutes ago!"

"You needn't mind the pie! I cant wait!"

"Bring me a ham-omelet, a cup of coffee, and some corn muffins! What? Well, send

hats] *the number '3' is interlined above the 'h'*
old] *interlined*
coffee, and] *'a' written over an illegible letter*

[leaf 55v]

4
the right waiter here then! I can't wait all day."

Meanwhile the waiters dashed about the room as if something threatened them and they were trying to escape through the walls. They carried incredible masses of dishes and threaded their swift ways with rare skill. And always from afar back, at the cummunications to the kitchen, came hoarse roars and screams in a long chorus, vehement and excited, like the cries of the officers of a ship in a squall.

"You will percieve," said

waiter] *the number* '4' *is interlined above the* 'te'
skill.] *interlined above deleted* 'speed'
cummunications] *the* 's' *is added*
screams] *the final* 's' *is written over deleted* 'in'; *Crane was probably going to write* 'screaming'
long] *the following words* 'and exciting' *are deleted*

[leaf 54^v]

5

the stranger, "that if the waiters could only be put upon a raised platform and armed with repeating rifles loaded with corn-muffins, butter cakes, Irish stew or whatever was in particular demand, the public would be saved this dreadful strife each day and as long as the waiters were fairly competent marksmen, each man could cease his worry for the affair would be conducted with great expedition. The only great difficulty would be when for instance a waiter would make an error and give an Irish

"that] *the number '5' is interlined above the first 't'*
marksmen,] *an apostrophe after the 'k' is deleted*
for instance] *interlined*

[leaf 53[v]]

6

stew to the wrong man. This latter would have considerable trouble in passing it along to the right one. Everybody, I think, would grow dexterous in catching their meals in these derby hats which you wear so much in the east. Of course, look all innovations, it would cause awkward blunders for a time. You can imagine an important-looking gentleman in a white waist-coat getting up to procure the bill-of-fare from the adjacent table and by chance intercepting a hamburger-steak

wrong] *the number* '6' *is interlined above the* 'o'

innovations,] *a following* 'there' *is deleted*

time.] *interlined above deleted* 'while'; *the* 'w' *in* 'while' *is written over a* 'b'

up] *written over* 'to'

[leaf 52v]

7
bound for a man down by the door. You see of course that the man down by the door would refuse to pay for a steak which had never come into his possession and this would entail a certain loss to the house. And then undoubtedly there would develope a certain class of unscrupulous persons, clever at catching liners right off the bat so to speak, who would stand up in the front rank and appropriate a good many orders that were meant for quiet citizens in the rear.

bound for] 'bound f' *is deleted in the line above* 'bound for'
a man] *the number* '7' *is written on the line above the* 'm'
possession] *interlined with a caret above deleted* 'position'
who would] 'would' *interlined*

[leaf 51v]

8

But after a time the laws would arise that always come to control these new inventions and the system would settle into something neat and swift. At these places where butter cakes are at a premium, batteries of rapid-fire ordnance could be erected to cammand every inch of floor-space and at a given signal, a destructive fire could sweep the entire establishment. I estimate that forty-two thousand people could be feed by this method in establishments which can

time] *the number '8' is written on the line above 't'*
signal,] *a following* 'the' *is deleted*

[leaf 50r]

9
now accomadate but from one of three hundred during the noon rush. Of course eloquent pickets would have to be stationed in the distance to intercept any unsuspecting gentlemen from the west who might resent what would look to them an assault and retort with western fervor. I remember that my old friend Jim Wilkinson, the sheriff of Tin Can, Nevada, got drunk one night and strolled into the business end of the bowling alley there. Of course he thought they were shooting

accomadate] *the number* '9' *is interlined above the* 't'
hundred] *a following* 'people' *is deleted*
gentlemen] 'en' *written over* 'a'
resent] *a following* 'the' *and the letters* 'ass' *are deleted*
what] *the following letters* 'loo' *are deleted*
remember] *a following* 'once' *is deleted*
alley] *a following period is deleted*

[leaf 49^v]

IO
at him and in reply he killed three of the best bowlers in
Tin Can!"

Once a man clambering to

in] *the number* 'IO' *is interlined above* 'in'

line 3] *written in lighter, sharper pencil than the preceding sketch* [leaf 48[v] is blank; between leaves 49 and 48 ten leaves are torn out.]

[leaf 47[v]]

"Huly gee! Everyting's dumped!"

"S'cuse me, gen'l'm'n fer bein' so noisy but I'm Republican! See? I'm Republican! What? Yessir! Morton by seventy-fi' thousan'. Yessir!

Can you tell me, please, do the returns indicate wether Goff has a chance?

"Who? Goff? Well I guess! He's running away ahead everywhere. He's dead in it!"

Not by a blame sight he didn't!

me] *interlined*
in it!"] *the following words* 'Say, how' *are deleted*

[leaf 46v]

"Oh, hurry up your old slide! Put on another! Good thing—push it along! Ah, there we are: 'Morton's plurality over Hill is estimated at 40135.' Say, look at that, would you? Don't talk to me about the unterrified Democracy. There's more run than fight in that crowd, you bet. Hey, hurry up, Willie, give us another one. It's a good thing but push it along!" Say, Strong has got a cinch! He wins in a walk! Ah, there, Hughey, ah there."

but] *a following* 'a' *is deleted*

[leaf 45v]

"Well, I guess nit! If Hill wins this time, he's got to have ice-boats on his feet. He aint got a chance.

"If Tammany wins this time we might as well all quit the town and go live in Jersey. If we don't beat 'em now, we're a lot duffers and we ought to be used to stuff mattresses with!"

Down in Fourteenth Street
Hear that mournful sound
All the Indians are a-weeping
Davie's in the cold, cold ground

a-weeping] 'a' *written over a hyphen*

[leaf 44v]

"Say, hear 'em yell for Goff! Popular? Well I should say!

Oh, what a roast—
Hully chee!
Who are we?
The men who did up Tammanee

He won't, hay? You just wait, me boy. If Hill cant carry this state at any time in any year, I'll make you a present of the Brooklyn bridge and paint it a deep purple with gold stripes all by myself."

I've only see two Dem—

Oh,] *on the line above* 'Oh,' *the words* 'Not on' *are deleted*
Oh,] 'X' *is written in ink before* 'Oh,'
Who] 'X' *is written in ink before* 'Who'
I've] 'X' *is written in ink before* 'I've'
Dem—] 'D' *is written over the beginning of an illegible letter*

[leaf 43r]

ocrats tonight. Theres another one. That makes three!

I'd like to see Dickie Croker now and ask him how he knew when to get in out of the wet! I'll tell you what it is—there's no use saying anything about Dickie's eye-sight."

"Oh, my, what a surprise! Little David Bennet Hill is now looking at himself with opera-glasses to see if

Well, this is what comes from monkeying with the people.

I'd] 'X' *is interlined in ink*
like to see] 'see' *interlined*

[leaf 42^v]

"There never was a minute"

"Little Goffie wasn't in it!"

Now I'll tell you just one thing—if this dont prove to politicans that you got to be always on the level, why, they're about as thickheaded a gang as there is on the face of the earth.

"Voorhis and Taintor! They're the only two! The rest—"

Who said Tammany couldn't be thrown down?

Grady did!

Ah there, Grady!

Now] 'X' *is written in ink before* 'Now'

politicans] *an* 'i' *between* 'c' *and* 'a' *is deleted*

face] *Crane wrote* 'surface' *and then deleted the* 'sur'

[leaf 41r]

In the dark hall-way of the tenement three woman were quarreling animatedly. Their gestures made enormous shadows that, further back, mingled in terrific combat.

A young girl came from the street and brushed past them on her way upstairs.

They wheeled then instantly to watch her and ceased quarreling temporaryily that they might criticise her

line 1] *two lines above this line Crane wrote, the title* 'D[is]covery of the Crime' *which he deleted*
line 1] *one line above this line someone other than Crane wrote in blue pencil* '[F]ist copt of a de-[ ]sertion'; *the handwriting resembles Cora Crane's*
animatedly.] *period written over deleted comma*
animatedly.] *a following* 'and' *is deleted*
Their] 'T' *written over* 't'
came] *a following* 'back' *is deleted*
on her] 'her' *written over* 'on'

[leaf 40^v]

face, her clothes, her manners. It was apparent that they thought she was superior to them in many ways. They were extremely vindictive.

The girl entered a room on the top floor of the house, bursting in with a joyous air, as one who was assured of a warm welcome. However, the room seemed empty and she hesitated near the threshold suddenly, giving vent to a little feminine cry. "Oh!"

There was before her a sombre gloom save where, from the front of

manners.] *a following* 'Mary' *is deleted*
thought she] *a following* 'must' *is deleted*
entered a] 'a' *written over the beginning of an illegible letter*
near] *interlined above deleted* 'on'

[leaf 39v]

the kitchen stove, there shone forth four little squares of crimson light.

The girl turned and looked down the stairs again. "I wonder where dad's gone," she said to herself. Then she turned and looked at the room again as if this silent interior could answer her question.

Presently she discerned a familar shape seated at the table with it's back turned to her. She had not discerned it in the shrouding shadows.

four] 'f' *written over the beginning of an illegible letter*
"I] *written over* 'P'
where] *Crane originally wrote* 'wheres' *and then deleted the* 's'

[leaf 38v]

She entered then with a repetition of her joyous cry. "Oh, daddie," she said, pouting "I thought you had gone out."

her] *a following* 'cry' *is deleted*
pouting] *the following words* 'at once now' *are deleted*

[leaf 37r]

A man and a boy were trudging slowly along an east-side street. It was nearly six o'clock in the evening and this street, which led to one of the East River Ferries was crowded with laborers, shop-men and shop women, hurrying to their dinners, made more eager by the recollections of their toil and by the shop-windows, glaring with light, suggesting those

evening] *the following words* 'in the [ ]' *are deleted*
Ferries] 'F' *written over* 'f'
shop-men] 'm' *written over* 'w'
and by the] *the following letters* 'glo' *are deleted*
suggesting] *a following* 'those' *and the letters* 'Engl' *are deleted*

[leaf 36v]

The man and the boy conversed in Italian, mumbling the soft syllables and making little quick egotistical gestures. Suddenly, the man glared, and wavered on his limbs for a moment as if some blinding light had flashed before his vision; then he swayed like a drunken man and fell. The boy grasped his arm convulsively and made an attempt to support his companion so that the body slid to the side-walk with an easy motion

line 1] *the following is interlined in pencil in handwriting similar to Cora Crane's:* '4 copies made Sep 18—1900 Two sent Reynolds serial & book'; '4' *is written over a word, possibly* 'Two'; *under* 'Reynolds' *the word* 'one' *is deleted.* Paul Reynolds was Crane's agent.

convulsively and] *the following words* 'made him' *are deleted*

[leaf 35[v]]

2

like a corpse sinking in the sea. The boy screamed.

Instantly, in all directions turned their gaze upon that figure prone upon the side-walk. In a moment there was a dodging, peering, pushing crowd about the man. A volley of questions, replies, speculations flew to and fro among all the bobbing heads.

"What's th' matter? What's th' matter"

"Oh, a jag, I guess!"

"Aw, he's got a fit!"

"What's th' matter! What's th' matter"

Two streams of people coming from different

corpse] *the number '2' is interlined above the 's'; this number and the following are in Crane's handwriting*

sinking in] 'to' *has been added to* 'in' *forming* 'into'; *the addition is made in the same pencil and handwriting as the addition on leaf 36[v]*

Instantly, in] *the same hand and pencil which made the addition in the note immediately above deleted* 'in' *and interlined* 'people from' above a caret

all] *interlined above a caret*

[leaf 34[v]]

3
directions met at this point to form a great crowd. Others came from across the street.

Down under their feet, almost lost under this mass of people, lay the man, hidden in the shadows caused by their forms which in fact barely allowed a particle of light to pass between them. Those in foremost rank bended down eagerly anxious to see everything. Others behind them crowded savagely like starving men fighting for bread. Always, the

met] *the number '3' is interlined above the 't'*

[leaf 33[v]]

4
question could be heard flying in the air. "What's th' matter?" Some, near to the body and perhaps feeling the danger of being forced over upon it, twisted their heads and protested violently to those unheeding ones who were scuffling in the rear. "Say, quit yer shovin', cant yeh? What do yeh want, anyhow? Quit!"

Somebody back in the throng suddenly said: "Say, young feller, cheese dat pushin! I aint no peach!"

Another voice said: "Well, dat's all right—"

could] *the number* '4' *is interlined above the* 'd'
dat] 'd' *written over* 'th'

[leaf 32v]

5

The boy who had been with the Italian, was standing helplessly, a frightened look in his eyes and holding the man's hand. Sometimes, he looked about him dumbly, with indefinite hope, as if he expected sudden assistance to come from the clouds. The men about him frequently jostled him until he was obliged to put his hand upon the breast of the body to maintain his balance. Those nearest the man upon the side-walk at first saw his body

who] *the number '5' is interlined above the 'h'*
The men] 'T' *written over* 'S'
jostled him] 'h' *written over part of an illegible letter*
maintain] *interlined above deleted* 'keep fro'
Those] 'o' *written over* 'e'; *a following* 'man' *is deleted; Crane originally wrote* 'The man'

[leaf 31v]

6

go through a singular contortion. It was as if an invisible hand had reached up from the earth and had seized him by the hair. He seemed dragged slowly pitilessly backward, while his body stiffened convulsively, his hands clenched and his arms swung rigidly upward. Through his pallid half-closed lids one could see the steel-colored, assassin-like gleam of his eye that shone with a mystic light as a corpse might glare at those live ones who seemed about to trample it under foot.

singular] *the number* '6' *is interlined above the* 'i'
upward] 'u' *written over a period*
steel-] *a following* 'like' *and the letters* 'feve' *and* 'wi' *are deleted*
as a] 'a' *interlined above deleted* 'the'
corpse] *interlined above deleted* 'dead'

[leaf 30r]

7

As for the men near, they hung back, appearing as if they expected it might spring erect and grab them. Their eyes however were held in a spell of fascination. They scarce seemed to breathe. They were contemplating a depth into which a human being had sunk and the marvel of this mystery of life or death held them chained. Occasionally from the rear, a man came thrusting his way impetuously, satisfied that there was a horror to be seen and apparently insane to

men] *the number* '7' *is interlined above the* 'n'
back,] *a following* 'afraid' *is deleted*
might] *a following* 'jump' *is deleted*
from] 'om' *written over* 'm'
way] *interlined above a caret*

[leaf 29^v]

get a view of it. More self-contained men swore at these persons when they tred upon their toes.

The street-cars jingled past this scene in endless parade. Occasionally, down where the elevated road crossed the street one could hear some times a thunder, suddenly begun and suddenly ended. Over the heads of the crowd hung an immovable canvas sign. "Regular dinner twenty cents."

The body on the pave seemed like a bit of debris

The] *the following letters* 'ho' *and the beginning of another letter, possibly* 'r', *are deleted*
scene] *the following words* 'in a' *are deleted*
canvas] 'nv' *written over* 'rv'
The] *a following* 'man' *is deleted*
body] 'd' *written over* 'l'

[leaf 28^v]

sunk in this human ocean.

But after the first spasm of curiosity had passed away, there were those in the crowd who began to bethink themselves of some way to help. A voice called out: "Rub his wrists." The boy and a man on the other side of the body began to rub the wrists and slap the palms of the man. A tall German suddenly appeared and resolutely began to push the crowd back. "Get back there —get back,"

But] *a following* 'it' *is deleted*
appeared and] *the following words* 'shouted out' *and the letters* 'excit' *are deleted*

[leaf 27[v]]

he repeated continually while he pushed at them. He seemed to have authority; the crowd obeyed him. He and another man knelt down by the man in the darkness and loosened his shirt at the throat. Once they struck a match and held it close to the man's face. This livid visage suddenly appearing under their feet in the light of the match's yellow glare, made the crowd shudder. Half articulate exclamations could be heard. There were men who nearly created a riot

by the man] 'man' *written over deleted* 'body'

match's] *the apostrophe written over an* 'e'

[leaf 26r]

in the madness of their desire to see the thing.

Meanwhile others had been questioning the boy. "What's his name? Where does he live?"

Then a policeman appeared. The first part of the little drama had gone on without his assistance but now he came, strideing swiftly, his helmet towering over the crowd and shading that impenetrable police face. He charged the crowd as if he were a squadron of Irish lancers. The people fairly withered before

does he] 'e' *written over* 'is'
He charged] *notable change from dark to light pencil*
people] *a following* 'were' *is deleted*

[leaf 25v]

this onslaught. Occasionally he shouted: “Come, make way there. Come now!” He was evidently a man whose life was half-pestered out of him by people who were sufficently unreasonable and stupid as to insist on walking in the streets. He felt the rage toward them that a placid cow feels toward the flies that hover in clouds and disturb their repose. When he arrived at the centre of the crowd he first said

[leaf 24r]

threateningly: ", What's th' matter here." And then when he saw that human bit of wreckage at the bottom of the sea of men he said to it: "Come, git up outa that! Git outa here!"

Whereupon hands were raised in the crowd and a volley of decorated information was blazed at the officer.

"Ah, he's got a fit! Cant yeh see!"

"He's got a fit!"

"What th' ell yeh doin'? Leave 'im be."

The policeman menaced

threateningly:"] *a following* 'Come' *is deleted; the comma before* 'What's' *belongs with* 'Come', *but Crane did not delete it*
What's] 'W' *written over* 'w'
doin' ?] '?' *written over* '!'
Leave] 'L' *written over the beginning of an illegible letter*

[leaf 23v]

with a glance the crowd from whose safe precincts the defiant voices had emerged.

A doctor had come. He and the policeman bended down at the man's side. Occasionally the officer reared up to create room. The crowd fell away before his admonitions, his threats, his sarcastic questions and before the sweep of those two huge buckskin gloves.

At last, the peering ones saw the man on the sidewalk begin to breathe heavily,

create] *Crane originally wrote* 'created' *and then deleted the* 'd'

[leaf 22r]

strainedly as if he had just come to the surface from some deep water. He uttered a low cry in his foriegn way. It was like a baby's squeal or the sade wail of a little storm-tossed kitten. As this cry went forth to all those eager ears the jostling, crowding, recommenced again furiously until the doctor was obliged to yell warningly a dozen times. The policeman had gone to send the ambulance call.

When a man struck

sade] 'a' *written over* 'i'; *Crane originally wrote* 'side', *but forgot to delete the* 'e' *when he added the* 'a'
wail] *interlined above deleted* 'moan'
doctor] 'o' *written over* 'e'

[leaf 21ᵛ]

another match and in it's meagre light the doctor felt the skull of the prostrate man carefully to discover if any wound had been caused by his fall to the stone side-walk, the crowd pressed and crushed again. It was as if they fully expected to see blood by the light of the match and the desire made them appear almost insane. The policeman returned and fought with them. The doctor looked up occasionally to scold

almost] 'a' *written over* 'i'

[leaf 20^{v}]

and demand room.

At last out the faint haze of light far up the street, there came the sound of a gong beaten rapidly impatiently. A monstrous truck loaded to the sky with barrels, scurried to one side with marvelous agility. And then the black wagon with it's gleam of gold lettering and bright brass gong clattered into view, the horse galloping. A young man, as always as if he were going

came the] *the following words* 'rapid impatient' *are deleted*
And] 'A' *written over the beginning of another letter, possibly* 'T'
view,] *comma written after a deleted period*
as] *a following* 'imperturbable' *is deleted*

[leaf 19^v]

on a picnic, sat thoughtfully upon the rear seat.

When they picked up the limp body, from which came little moans and howls, the crowd almost turned into a mob. When the ambulance started on it's banging and clanging return, they stood and gazed until it was quite out of sight. Some resumed their ways with an air of relief. Others still continued to stare after the vanished

read] *a following* 'side-walk.' *is deleted*
quite] 'q' *written over* 'a'

[leaf 18v]

ambulance and it's burden as if they had been cheated, as if the curtain had been rung down on a tragedy that was but half completed and this impenetrable blanket intervening between a sufferer and their curiosity, seemed to make them feel an injustice.

on a] *a following* 'journey' *is deleted*

[leaves 17–15 blank; leaves 14^v–1^v blank. Between 18 and 17 one leaf torn out; between 17 and 16 six leaves torn out.]

The Notebook of Stephen Crane

was composed, printed, and bound by
Kingsport Press, Inc., Kingsport, Tennessee
in an edition of 750 copies.
The text paper is Curtis Rag.
The French marble paper was supplied by
Andrews/Nelson/Whitehead.
The type is Rudolph Ruzicka's Primer.
Designer: Edward G. Foss
General Editor: Walker Cowen